POWER
CAREER
WOMAN

A 52-Week Guided Journal
for Career Success

Dedication

I dedicate this book to my mother, Diane Harmon, who has always been my most faithful cheerleader. Thank you for praying for me, raising me to work hard, and be courageous enough to pursue God's plan for my life. The grit in me was birthed through you.

Love,

Tonya

Introduction

I created this journal to guide your thoughts and actions toward realizing the career success of your dreams.

Throughout the year, it's easy for you to get distracted from taking actions that advance your career in a meaningful way. Challenges come, disappointments arise, and sometimes encouragement is hard to come by. This journal will keep you on track, week to week, in a way that allows you to stay focused and inspired to move towards your career goals. When your mindset is programmed to see the best of possibilities, your career will follow suit.

Turn to this journal a few times a week, each week throughout the year. It will guide you in thoughtful reflection, affirmation and self-discovery that will motivate you to keep moving towards your biggest career goals. With this journal by your side, you will find yourself making progress all year long.

Tonya N. Sloans, Esq.

Week 1

/ /

BELIEVE THAT YOUR DREAM CAREER IS POSSIBLE.
GRATITUDE & POSITIVE WORDS
AFFIRM YOUR BELIEF.

Gratitude

What three things are you grateful for this week?

Affirmation

What is your affirmation of the week?

Reflection

What was the best part of your work week?

YOU WERE CREATED BY GOD, THE PERFECT MANUFACTURER, WHO MAKES NO MISTAKES. WHAT DOES THAT SAY ABOUT YOU?

_____

_____

_____

_____

_____

_____

_____

_____

_____

_____

_____

_____

_____

_____

_____

_____

_____

_____

_____

_____

Week 2   /   /

BELIEVE THAT YOUR DREAM CAREER IS POSSIBLE.
GRATITUDE & POSITIVE WORDS
AFFIRM YOUR BELIEF.

Gratitude

What three things are you grateful for this week?

Affirmation

What is your affirmation of the week?

Reflection

What was the best part of your work week?

HAVE YOU INVESTED TIME UNCOVERING THE BEST CAREER FIT FOR YOURSELF? FORTY YEARS OF EMPLOYMENT IS A LONG TIME TO SPEND AS A MISFIT.

_____

_____

_____

_____

_____

_____

_____

_____

_____

_____

_____

_____

_____

_____

_____

_____

_____

_____

_____

Week 3

BELIEVE THAT YOUR DREAM CAREER IS POSSIBLE.
GRATITUDE & POSITIVE WORDS
AFFIRM YOUR BELIEF.

Gratitude

What three things are you grateful for this week?

Affirmation

What is your affirmation of the week?

Reflection

What was the best part of your work week?

IT'S NEVER TOO LATE TO BECOME A NEW YOU. WHAT PARTS OF YOU DO YOU WANT TO MAKE BRAND NEW?

Week 4 / /

BELIEVE THAT YOUR DREAM CAREER IS POSSIBLE.
GRATITUDE & POSITIVE WORDS
AFFIRM YOUR BELIEF.

Gratitude

What three things are you grateful for this week?

Affirmation

What is your affirmation of the week?

Reflection

What was the best part of your work week?

YOUR VOICE IS YOUR POWER.
ARE YOU USING YOUR POWER?

_____

_____

_____

_____

_____

_____

_____

_____

_____

_____

_____

_____

_____

_____

_____

_____

_____

_____

_____

_____

Week 5 / /

BELIEVE THAT YOUR DREAM CAREER IS POSSIBLE.
GRATITUDE & POSITIVE WORDS
AFFIRM YOUR BELIEF.

Gratitude

What three things are you grateful for this week?

Affirmation

What is your affirmation of the week?

Reflection

What was the best part of your work week?

NO JOB COULD POSSIBLY SATISFY EVERY HUMAN NEED. ARE YOU EXPECTING YOUR JOB TO FULFILL ALL OF YOUR NEEDS?

_____

_____

_____

_____

_____

_____

_____

_____

_____

_____

_____

_____

_____

_____

_____

_____

_____

_____

_____

_____

Week 6 / /

BELIEVE THAT YOUR DREAM CAREER IS POSSIBLE.
GRATITUDE & POSITIVE WORDS
AFFIRM YOUR BELIEF.

Gratitude

What three things are you grateful for this week?

Affirmation

What is your affirmation of the week?

Reflection

What was the best part of your work week?

CHOOSE TO BE HAPPY RIGHT WHERE YOU ARE NOW. WHAT REASONS DO YOU HAVE TO BE HAPPY?

_____

_____

_____

_____

_____

_____

_____

_____

_____

_____

_____

_____

_____

_____

_____

_____

_____

_____

_____

Week 7   / /

BELIEVE THAT YOUR DREAM CAREER IS POSSIBLE.
GRATITUDE & POSITIVE WORDS
AFFIRM YOUR BELIEF.

Gratitude

What three things are you grateful for this week?

Affirmation

What is your affirmation of the week?

Reflection

What was the best part of your work week?

THERE IS POWER IN PREPARATION.
HOW CAN YOU PREPARE FOR THE POWER CAREER
THAT YOU WANT?

Week 8 ___/___/___

BELIEVE THAT YOUR DREAM CAREER IS POSSIBLE.
GRATITUDE & POSITIVE WORDS
AFFIRM YOUR BELIEF.

Gratitude

What three things are you grateful for this week?

Affirmation

What is your affirmation of the week?

Reflection

What was the best part of your work week?

EVEN IF THINGS GET BUSY, DON'T ELIMINATE TIME TO
MAKE MOVES TO ADVANCE YOUR CAREER.
WHAT MOVES ARE YOU COMMITTED TO MAKING?

_____

_____

_____

_____

_____

_____

_____

_____

_____

_____

_____

_____

_____

_____

_____

_____

_____

_____

_____

_____

Week 9 / /

BELIEVE THAT YOUR DREAM CAREER IS POSSIBLE.
GRATITUDE & POSITIVE WORDS
AFFIRM YOUR BELIEF.

Gratitude

What three things are you grateful for this week?

Affirmation

What is your affirmation of the week?

Reflection

What was the best part of your work week?

THINK ABOUT WHAT YOU WANT YOUR CAREER TO
LOOK LIKE DOWN THE ROAD. WHAT
VISION WILL YOU PURSUE WITH ALL YOUR MIGHT?

_____

_____

_____

_____

_____

_____

_____

_____

_____

_____

_____

_____

_____

_____

_____

_____

_____

_____

_____

Week 10

 / /

BELIEVE THAT YOUR DREAM CAREER IS POSSIBLE.
GRATITUDE & POSITIVE WORDS
AFFIRM YOUR BELIEF.

Gratitude

What three things are you grateful for this week?

Affirmation

*What is your affirmation of
the week?*

Reflection

*What was the best part of
your work week?*

WARNING: EVERYONE AROUND YOU WON'T CELEBRATE YOUR ATTEMPTS TO MOVE YOUR CAREER FORWARD. HOW CAN YOU PRESS FORWARD ANYWAY?

_____

_____

_____

_____

_____

_____

_____

_____

_____

_____

_____

_____

_____

_____

_____

_____

_____

_____

_____

_____

Week 11

BELIEVE THAT YOUR DREAM CAREER IS POSSIBLE.
GRATITUDE & POSITIVE WORDS
AFFIRM YOUR BELIEF.

Gratitude

What three things are you grateful for this week?

Affirmation

What is your affirmation of the week?

Reflection

What was the best part of your work week?

ARE YOU IN THE RIGHT INDUSTRY TO MAKE THE MONEY YOU WANT TO MAKE?

_____

_____

_____

_____

_____

_____

_____

_____

_____

_____

_____

_____

_____

_____

_____

_____

_____

_____

_____

_____

Week 12   / /

BELIEVE THAT YOUR DREAM CAREER IS POSSIBLE.
GRATITUDE & POSITIVE WORDS
AFFIRM YOUR BELIEF.

Gratitude

What three things are you grateful for this week?

Affirmation

What is your affirmation of the week?

Reflection

What was the best part of your work week?

YOU DON'T ALWAYS NEED TO KNOW EVERY STEP OF YOUR PROCESS BEFORE YOU START. HOW CAN YOU TAKE A STEP BY FAITH?

_____

_____

_____

_____

_____

_____

_____

_____

_____

_____

_____

_____

_____

_____

_____

_____

_____

_____

_____

_____

_____

Week 13 / /

BELIEVE THAT YOUR DREAM CAREER IS POSSIBLE.
GRATITUDE & POSITIVE WORDS
AFFIRM YOUR BELIEF.

Gratitude

What three things are you grateful for this week?

Affirmation

What is your affirmation of the week?

Reflection

What was the best part of your work week?

YOUR CAREER COULD BE IN A
WHOLE NEW PLACE 6 MONTHS FROM NOW.
WHAT CAN YOU START PLANNING NOW?

_____

_____

_____

_____

_____

_____

_____

_____

_____

_____

_____

_____

_____

_____

_____

_____

_____

_____

_____

Week 14

/ /

BELIEVE THAT YOUR DREAM CAREER IS POSSIBLE.
GRATITUDE & POSITIVE WORDS
AFFIRM YOUR BELIEF.

Gratitude

What three things are you grateful for this week?

Affirmation

*What is your affirmation of
the week?*

Reflection

*What was the best part of
your work week?*

DON'T DESPISE HUMBLE CAREER BEGINNINGS. THEY PREPARE YOU FOR YOUR DREAM OPPORTUNITY. ARE YOU APPRECIATIVE OF YOUR BEGINNINGS?

_____

_____

_____

_____

_____

_____

_____

_____

_____

_____

_____

_____

_____

_____

_____

_____

_____

_____

Week 15 / /

BELIEVE THAT YOUR DREAM CAREER IS POSSIBLE.
GRATITUDE & POSITIVE WORDS
AFFIRM YOUR BELIEF.

Gratitude

What three things are you grateful for this week?

Affirmation

What is your affirmation of the week?

Reflection

What was the best part of your work week?

WHEN DISAPPOINTING CIRCUMSTANCES SEEM TO TAKE YOUR CAREER BY STORM, SEARCH FOR AN UNUSUAL OPPORTUNITY. DO YOU SEE IT?

_____

_____

_____

_____

_____

_____

_____

_____

_____

_____

_____

_____

_____

_____

_____

_____

_____

_____

Week 16

BELIEVE THAT YOUR DREAM CAREER IS POSSIBLE.
GRATITUDE & POSITIVE WORDS
AFFIRM YOUR BELIEF.

Gratitude

What three things are you grateful for this week?

Affirmation

What is your affirmation of the week?

Reflection

What was the best part of your work week?

HAS YOUR CAREER DRIFTED AWAY FROM YOUR ORIGINAL CAREER GOALS? REFOCUS YOUR CAREER PATH BEFORE REGRET SETS IN.

_____

_____

_____

_____

_____

_____

_____

_____

_____

_____

_____

_____

_____

_____

_____

_____

_____

_____

Week 17 / /

BELIEVE THAT YOUR DREAM CAREER IS POSSIBLE.
GRATITUDE & POSITIVE WORDS
AFFIRM YOUR BELIEF.

Gratitude

What three things are you grateful for this week?

Affirmation

What is your affirmation of the week?

Reflection

What was the best part of your work week?

DO THE PEOPLE AROUND YOU EXCEL IN THEIR CAREERS? THOSE ARE THE KIND OF PEOPLE WHO WILL LET YOU BE GREAT IN YOUR CAREER.

_____

_____

_____

_____

_____

_____

_____

_____

_____

_____

_____

_____

_____

_____

_____

_____

_____

_____

_____

_____

Week 18   /   /

BELIEVE THAT YOUR DREAM CAREER IS POSSIBLE.
GRATITUDE & POSITIVE WORDS
AFFIRM YOUR BELIEF.

Gratitude

What three things are you grateful for this week?

Affirmation

What is your affirmation of the week?

Reflection

What was the best part of your work week?

YOUR BRAIN IS THE MOST SOPHISTICATED COMPUTER ON EARTH. ARE YOU MAXIMIZING ITS POTENTIAL?

_____

_____

_____

_____

_____

_____

_____

_____

_____

_____

_____

_____

_____

_____

_____

_____

_____

_____

_____

Week 19   /   /

BELIEVE THAT YOUR DREAM CAREER IS POSSIBLE.
GRATITUDE & POSITIVE WORDS
AFFIRM YOUR BELIEF.

Gratitude

What three things are you grateful for this week?

Affirmation

What is your affirmation of the week?

Reflection

What was the best part of your work week?

ARE YOU BEING SELFISH? DON'T BE SELFISH.
SHARE YOUR GIFTS AND TALENTS WITH THE WORLD.

_____

_____

_____

_____

_____

_____

_____

_____

_____

_____

_____

_____

_____

_____

_____

_____

_____

_____

Week 20 / /

BELIEVE THAT YOUR DREAM CAREER IS POSSIBLE.
GRATITUDE & POSITIVE WORDS
AFFIRM YOUR BELIEF.

Gratitude

What three things are you grateful for this week?

Affirmation

What is your affirmation of the week?

Reflection

What was the best part of your work week?

RELATIONSHIPS ARE IMPORTANT IN CAREER ADVANCEMENT. ARE YOU SHARING AND RECEIVING SUPPORT FROM YOUR GIRLFRIENDS IN THIS AREA?

_____

_____

_____

_____

_____

_____

_____

_____

_____

_____

_____

_____

_____

_____

_____

_____

_____

_____

Week 21   / /

BELIEVE THAT YOUR DREAM CAREER IS POSSIBLE.
GRATITUDE & POSITIVE WORDS
AFFIRM YOUR BELIEF.

Gratitude

What three things are you grateful for this week?

Affirmation

What is your affirmation of the week?

Reflection

What was the best part of your work week?

PROFESSIONAL VALUE TRANSLATES INTO EARNINGS AND WEALTH. HOW CAN YOU PRIORITIZE CAREER DEVELOPMENT AS A WEALTH-BUILDING STRATEGY?

Week 22

/ /

BELIEVE THAT YOUR DREAM CAREER IS POSSIBLE.
GRATITUDE & POSITIVE WORDS
AFFIRM YOUR BELIEF.

Gratitude

What three things are you grateful for this week?

Affirmation

What is your affirmation of the week?

Reflection

What was the best part of your work week?

EVEN THE STRONGEST POWERWOMAN ASKS FOR HELP FROM TIME TO TIME. HAVE YOU ASKED FOR THE HELP YOU NEED TO REACH YOUR CAREER GOALS?

_____

_____

_____

_____

_____

_____

_____

_____

_____

_____

_____

_____

_____

_____

_____

_____

Week 23 / /

BELIEVE THAT YOUR DREAM CAREER IS POSSIBLE.
GRATITUDE & POSITIVE WORDS
AFFIRM YOUR BELIEF.

Gratitude

What three things are you grateful for this week?

Affirmation

What is your affirmation of the week?

Reflection

What was the best part of your work week?

EVERY TIME YOUR DREAM COMES TO YOUR MIND, IT'S A SWEET REMINDER FROM GOD THAT IT IS POSSIBLE. HAVE YOU FULLY EMBRACED YOUR CAREER DREAM?

_____

_____

_____

_____

_____

_____

_____

_____

_____

_____

_____

_____

_____

_____

_____

_____

_____

_____

Week 24 / /

BELIEVE THAT YOUR DREAM CAREER IS POSSIBLE.
GRATITUDE & POSITIVE WORDS
AFFIRM YOUR BELIEF.

Gratitude

What three things are you grateful for this week?

Affirmation

What is your affirmation of the week?

Reflection

What was the best part of your work week?

LIFE'S TROUBLES ARE ONLY TEMPORARY. HAVE YOU GIVEN THEM A PERMANENT PLACE IN YOUR LIFE?

_____

_____

_____

_____

_____

_____

_____

_____

_____

_____

_____

_____

_____

_____

_____

_____

_____

_____

Week 25 / /

BELIEVE THAT YOUR DREAM CAREER IS POSSIBLE.
GRATITUDE & POSITIVE WORDS
AFFIRM YOUR BELIEF.

Gratitude

What three things are you grateful for this week?

Affirmation

What is your affirmation of the week?

Reflection

What was the best part of your work week?

HAVE YOU REACHED THE END OF YOUR LIFE?
IF NOT, JUST REACH HIGHER.
THERE IS STILL TIME TO DO SOMETHING GREAT.

_____

_____

_____

_____

_____

_____

_____

_____

_____

_____

_____

_____

_____

_____

_____

_____

_____

_____

_____

Week 26   /   /

BELIEVE THAT YOUR DREAM CAREER IS POSSIBLE.
GRATITUDE & POSITIVE WORDS
AFFIRM YOUR BELIEF.

Gratitude

What three things are you grateful for this week?

Affirmation

What is your affirmation of the week?

Reflection

What was the best part of your work week?

FRIENSHIPS HAVE THE POWER TO INFLUENCE YOUR ABILITY TO ACHIEVE YOUR GOALS.
HOW ARE YOUR FRIENDSHIPS INFLUENCING YOU?

_____

_____

_____

_____

_____

_____

_____

_____

_____

_____

_____

_____

_____

_____

_____

_____

_____

Week 27 / /

BELIEVE THAT YOUR DREAM CAREER IS POSSIBLE.
GRATITUDE & POSITIVE WORDS
AFFIRM YOUR BELIEF.

Gratitude

What three things are you grateful for this week?

Affirmation

What is your affirmation of the week?

Reflection

What was the best part of your work week?

IF YOU THINK YOU CAN DO SOMETHING, YOU LIKELY CAN, BUT YOU WON'T KNOW FOR SURE UNTIL YOU GIVE IT A TRY. WHAT ARE YOU WILLING TO TRY?

_____

_____

_____

_____

_____

_____

_____

_____

_____

_____

_____

_____

_____

_____

_____

_____

_____

_____

_____

Week 28

/ /

BELIEVE THAT YOUR DREAM CAREER IS POSSIBLE.
GRATITUDE & POSITIVE WORDS
AFFIRM YOUR BELIEF.

Gratitude

What three things are you grateful for this week?

Affirmation

What is your affirmation of the week?

Reflection

What was the best part of your work week?

DREAMS DON'T WORK UNLESS YOU DO THE WORK.
WHAT ARE YOU GOING TO DO THIS WEEK?

_____

_____

_____

_____

_____

_____

_____

_____

_____

_____

_____

_____

_____

_____

_____

_____

_____

Week 29

BELIEVE THAT YOUR DREAM CAREER IS POSSIBLE.
GRATITUDE & POSITIVE WORDS
AFFIRM YOUR BELIEF.

Gratitude

What three things are you grateful for this week?

Affirmation

What is your affirmation of the week?

Reflection

What was the best part of your work week?

YOU ARE BLESSED TO BE YOU!
WHICH OF YOUR CHARACTER TRAITS WILL HELP YOU REACH THE CAREER SUCCESS YOU DESIRE?

_____

_____

_____

_____

_____

_____

_____

_____

_____

_____

_____

_____

_____

_____

_____

_____

_____

_____

_____

Week 30   /   /

BELIEVE THAT YOUR DREAM CAREER IS POSSIBLE.
GRATITUDE & POSITIVE WORDS
AFFIRM YOUR BELIEF.

Gratitude

What three things are you grateful for this week?

Affirmation

What is your affirmation of the week?

Reflection

What was the best part of your work week?

A SOUR ATTITUDE WILL ONLY ZAP THE STRENGTH YOU
NEED TO ADVANCE YOUR CAREER. WHAT CAN
HELP YOU KEEP A POSITIVE ATTITUDE AT WORK?

_____

_____

_____

_____

_____

_____

_____

_____

_____

_____

_____

_____

_____

_____

_____

_____

_____

_____

_____

Week 31   /   /

BELIEVE THAT YOUR DREAM CAREER IS POSSIBLE.
GRATITUDE & POSITIVE WORDS
AFFIRM YOUR BELIEF.

Gratitude

What three things are you grateful for this week?

Affirmation

What is your affirmation of the week?

Reflection

What was the best part of your work week?

PEOPLE OFTEN COMMUNICATE
WITHOUT USING WORDS.
HAVE YOU LEARNED TO READ BEHAVIOR AT WORK?

_____

_____

_____

_____

_____

_____

_____

_____

_____

_____

_____

_____

_____

_____

_____

_____

_____

_____

Week 32   / /

BELIEVE THAT YOUR DREAM CAREER IS POSSIBLE.
GRATITUDE & POSITIVE WORDS
AFFIRM YOUR BELIEF.

Gratitude

What three things are you grateful for this week?

Affirmation

What is your affirmation of the week?

Reflection

What was the best part of your work week?

SELF-DOUBT IS ONE OF THE LEADING STUMBLING BLOCKS TO CAREER ADVANCEMENT FOR WOMEN. IS IT HOLDING YOU BACK?

_____

_____

_____

_____

_____

_____

_____

_____

_____

_____

_____

_____

_____

_____

_____

_____

_____

_____

_____

Week 33

BELIEVE THAT YOUR DREAM CAREER IS POSSIBLE.
GRATITUDE & POSITIVE WORDS
AFFIRM YOUR BELIEF.

Gratitude

What three things are you grateful for this week?

Affirmation

What is your affirmation of the week?

Reflection

What was the best part of your work week?

DILIGENCE BRINGS REWARD.
IS YOUR LEVEL OF DILIGENCE APPROPRIATE FOR THE REWARD YOU EXPECT?

_____

_____

_____

_____

_____

_____

_____

_____

_____

_____

_____

_____

_____

_____

_____

_____

_____

_____

Week 34 / /

BELIEVE THAT YOUR DREAM CAREER IS POSSIBLE.
GRATITUDE & POSITIVE WORDS
AFFIRM YOUR BELIEF.

Gratitude

What three things are you grateful for this week?

Affirmation

*What is your affirmation of
the week?*

Reflection

*What was the best part of
your work week?*

DOES YOUR WORK ETHIC MATCH YOUR INCOME?
IF NOT, ONE OF THEM MUST CHANGE.

_____

_____

_____

_____

_____

_____

_____

_____

_____

_____

_____

_____

_____

_____

_____

_____

_____

_____

_____

Week 35   /   /

BELIEVE THAT YOUR DREAM CAREER IS POSSIBLE.
GRATITUDE & POSITIVE WORDS
AFFIRM YOUR BELIEF.

Gratitude

What three things are you grateful for this week?

Affirmation

What is your affirmation of the week?

Reflection

What was the best part of your work week?

PATIENCE PAYS.
ARE YOU EMPLOYING PATIENCE?

_____

_____

_____

_____

_____

_____

_____

_____

_____

_____

_____

_____

_____

_____

_____

_____

_____

_____

Week 36 / /

BELIEVE THAT YOUR DREAM CAREER IS POSSIBLE.
GRATITUDE & POSITIVE WORDS
AFFIRM YOUR BELIEF.

Gratitude

What three things are you grateful for this week?

Affirmation

What is your affirmation of the week?

Reflection

What was the best part of your work week?

DO YOU WANT TO STAY STUCK RIGHT WHERE YOU ARE? IF SO, JUST LET YOURSELF GET TOO BUSY TO MAKE YOUR NEXT MOVE.

_____

_____

_____

_____

_____

_____

_____

_____

_____

_____

_____

_____

_____

_____

_____

_____

_____

_____

_____

Week 37   /   /

BELIEVE THAT YOUR DREAM CAREER IS POSSIBLE.
GRATITUDE & POSITIVE WORDS
AFFIRM YOUR BELIEF.

Gratitude

What three things are you grateful for this week?

Affirmation

What is your affirmation of the week?

Reflection

What was the best part of your work week?

IS THIS THE FIRST TIME YOU'VE ENCOUNTERED A
CHALLENGE AND OVERCOME? OF COURSE NOT.
REFLECT ON HOW YOU OVERCAME PAST TRIALS.

_____

_____

_____

_____

_____

_____

_____

_____

_____

_____

_____

_____

_____

_____

_____

_____

_____

_____

Week 38 / /

BELIEVE THAT YOUR DREAM CAREER IS POSSIBLE.
GRATITUDE & POSITIVE WORDS
AFFIRM YOUR BELIEF.

Gratitude

What three things are you grateful for this week?

Affirmation

What is your affirmation of the week?

Reflection

What was the best part of your work week?

WHAT WOULD BE DIFFERENT ABOUT YOUR LIFE IF YOU VIEWED YOUR CAREER AS A CALLING?

_____

_____

_____

_____

_____

_____

_____

_____

_____

_____

_____

_____

_____

_____

_____

_____

_____

_____

Week 39 / /

BELIEVE THAT YOUR DREAM CAREER IS POSSIBLE.
GRATITUDE & POSITIVE WORDS
AFFIRM YOUR BELIEF.

Gratitude

What three things are you grateful for this week?

Affirmation

What is your affirmation of the week?

Reflection

What was the best part of your work week?

WHILE YOU ARE WAITING FOR GOD TO MOVE IN YOUR LIFE, MAGNIFY HOPE. ARE YOU WHOLEHEARTEDLY FOCUSED ON THINGS WORKING OUT WELL?

_____

_____

_____

_____

_____

_____

_____

_____

_____

_____

_____

_____

_____

_____

_____

_____

_____

_____

_____

Week 40 / /

BELIEVE THAT YOUR DREAM CAREER IS POSSIBLE.
GRATITUDE & POSITIVE WORDS
AFFIRM YOUR BELIEF.

Gratitude

What three things are you grateful for this week?

Affirmation

What is your affirmation of the week?

Reflection

What was the best part of your work week?

PEOPLE YOU MEET IN A SOCIAL CONTEXT CAN BECOME BUSINESS CONTACTS.
ARE YOU MAXIMIZING SOCIAL OPPORTUNITIES?

_____

_____

_____

_____

_____

_____

_____

_____

_____

_____

_____

_____

_____

_____

_____

_____

_____

_____

_____

_____

Week 41

BELIEVE THAT YOUR DREAM CAREER IS POSSIBLE.
GRATITUDE & POSITIVE WORDS
AFFIRM YOUR BELIEF.

Gratitude

What three things are you grateful for this week?

Affirmation

What is your affirmation of the week?

Reflection

What was the best part of your work week?

WHEN LIFE GETS TOUGH, YOU MUST GET TOUGHER. HOW CAN YOU EXERCISE YOUR PERSONAL POWER WHEN CHALLENGES ARISE?

_____

_____

_____

_____

_____

_____

_____

_____

_____

_____

_____

_____

_____

_____

_____

_____

_____

_____

_____

_____

Week 42   /   /

BELIEVE THAT YOUR DREAM CAREER IS POSSIBLE.
GRATITUDE & POSITIVE WORDS
AFFIRM YOUR BELIEF.

Gratitude

What three things are you grateful for this week?

Affirmation

What is your affirmation of the week?

Reflection

What was the best part of your work week?

DON'T ACCEPT A MEDIOCRE CAREER. ARE YOU STRIVING TO MAXIMIZE YOUR CAREER POTENTIAL?

Week 43   /   /

BELIEVE THAT YOUR DREAM CAREER IS POSSIBLE.
GRATITUDE & POSITIVE WORDS
AFFIRM YOUR BELIEF.

Gratitude

What three things are you grateful for this week?

Affirmation

What is your affirmation of the week?

Reflection

What was the best part of your work week?

YOU NEED POSITIVE INFLUENCES TO SUPPORT YOU AS YOU ASCEND IN YOUR CAREER. DO YOUR CIRCLE OF FRIENDS ENCOURAGE PROFESSIONAL SUCCESS?

Week 44 / /

BELIEVE THAT YOUR DREAM CAREER IS POSSIBLE.
GRATITUDE & POSITIVE WORDS
AFFIRM YOUR BELIEF.

Gratitude

What three things are you grateful for this week?

Affirmation

What is your affirmation of the week?

Reflection

What was the best part of your work week?

YOU CAN FIND REST IN GOD THAT WILL CATAPULT YOU TO YOUR NEXT LEVEL, EFFORTLESSLY.
HAVE YOU FOUND THAT REST?

_____

_____

_____

_____

_____

_____

_____

_____

_____

_____

_____

_____

_____

_____

_____

_____

_____

_____

_____

_____

Week 45   / /

BELIEVE THAT YOUR DREAM CAREER IS POSSIBLE.
GRATITUDE & POSITIVE WORDS
AFFIRM YOUR BELIEF.

Gratitude

What three things are you grateful for this week?

Affirmation

What is your affirmation of the week?

Reflection

What was the best part of your work week?

YOU DESERVE YOUR OWN FORGIVENESS.
HAVE YOU MADE MISTAKES IN YOUR CAREER FOR WHICH YOU HAVE YET TO FORGIVE YOURSELF?

_____

_____

_____

_____

_____

_____

_____

_____

_____

_____

_____

_____

_____

_____

_____

_____

_____

_____

_____

Week 46 / /

BELIEVE THAT YOUR DREAM CAREER IS POSSIBLE.
GRATITUDE & POSITIVE WORDS
AFFIRM YOUR BELIEF.

Gratitude

What three things are you grateful for this week?

Affirmation

What is your affirmation of the week?

Reflection

What was the best part of your work week?

BIG DREAMS OFTEN START SMALL.
WHAT SMALL STEPS CAN YOU TAKE NOW TO ACHIEVE YOUR ULTIMATE CAREER GOAL?

_____

_____

_____

_____

_____

_____

_____

_____

_____

_____

_____

_____

_____

_____

_____

_____

_____

_____

_____

_____

Week 47 / /

BELIEVE THAT YOUR DREAM CAREER IS POSSIBLE.
GRATITUDE & POSITIVE WORDS
AFFIRM YOUR BELIEF.

Gratitude

What three things are you grateful for this week?

Affirmation

What is your affirmation of the week?

Reflection

What was the best part of your work week?

GOD'S POWER IS MADE PERFECT IN WEAKNESS. HAVE YOU SURRENDERED YOUR WEAKNESS TO HIS POWER?

_____

_____

_____

_____

_____

_____

_____

_____

_____

_____

_____

_____

_____

_____

_____

_____

_____

_____

_____

_____

Week 48 / /

BELIEVE THAT YOUR DREAM CAREER IS POSSIBLE.
GRATITUDE & POSITIVE WORDS
AFFIRM YOUR BELIEF.

Gratitude

What three things are you grateful for this week?

Affirmation

What is your affirmation of the week?

Reflection

What was the best part of your work week?

WHEN YOU KNOW WHO YOU ARE, YOU REFUSE
EMPLOYMENT MISALIGNED WITH YOUR POTENTIAL.
DOES YOUR CAREER REFLECT YOUR IDENTITY?

_____

_____

_____

_____

_____

_____

_____

_____

_____

_____

_____

_____

_____

_____

_____

_____

_____

_____

Week 49   / /

BELIEVE THAT YOUR DREAM CAREER IS POSSIBLE.
GRATITUDE & POSITIVE WORDS
AFFIRM YOUR BELIEF.

Gratitude

What three things are you grateful for this week?

Affirmation

*What is your affirmation of
the week?*

Reflection

*What was the best part of
your work week?*

YOUR BRAIN WILL NEVER REACH MAXIMUM CAPACITY.
YOU WERE BUILT TO EXPAND, STRETCH, AND GROW.
HAVE YOU LIMITED YOURSELF UNNECESSARILY?

_____
_____
_____
_____
_____
_____
_____
_____
_____
_____
_____
_____
_____
_____
_____
_____
_____
_____
_____
_____
_____

Week 50

BELIEVE THAT YOUR DREAM CAREER IS POSSIBLE.
GRATITUDE & POSITIVE WORDS
AFFIRM YOUR BELIEF.

Gratitude

What three things are you grateful for this week?

Affirmation

What is your affirmation of the week?

Reflection

What was the best part of your work week?

WRESTLING WITH THE STRUGGLES OF LIFE ACTUALLY STRENGTHENS YOU. ARE YOU RUNNING FROM YOUR STRUGGLES OR LEANING IN?

_____

_____

_____

_____

_____

_____

_____

_____

_____

_____

_____

_____

_____

_____

_____

_____

_____

_____

_____

_____

Week 51

BELIEVE THAT YOUR DREAM CAREER IS POSSIBLE.
GRATITUDE & POSITIVE WORDS
AFFIRM YOUR BELIEF.

Gratitude

What three things are you grateful for this week?

Affirmation

What is your affirmation of the week?

Reflection

What was the best part of your work week?

THERE IS A GREAT, BIG WORLD OF OPPORTUNITY.
ARE YOU PLAYING SMALL IN YOUR CAREER?

_____

_____

_____

_____

_____

_____

_____

_____

_____

_____

_____

_____

_____

_____

_____

_____

_____

_____

Week 52 / /

BELIEVE THAT YOUR DREAM CAREER IS POSSIBLE.
GRATITUDE & POSITIVE WORDS
AFFIRM YOUR BELIEF.

Gratitude

What three things are you grateful for this week?

Affirmation

What is your affirmation of the week?

Reflection

What was the best part of your work week?

YOU MUST SEE YOURSELF OPERATING AT A HIGHER LEVEL BEFORE IT MANIFESTS.
HOW DO YOU SEE YOURSELF RIGHT NOW?

_____

_____

_____

_____

_____

_____

_____

_____

_____

_____

_____

_____

_____

_____

_____

_____

_____

_____

This is me.
Walking in purpose.
Standing for women who know they have untapped potential that can advance their careers.
I'm committed to using my God-inspired knowledge, training, education, and experience to help women rise to power in the workplace. Join me!!! Become the very best #powerwoman you can be!!!

Tonya N. Sloans, Esq.

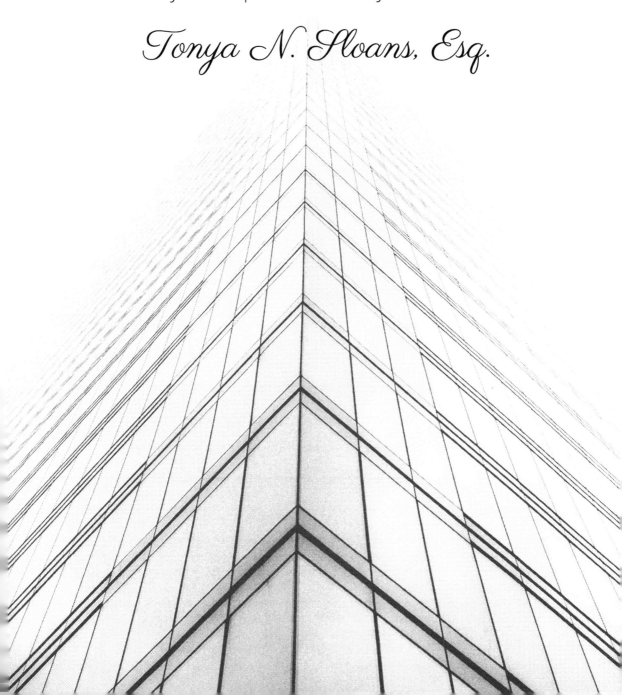

Made in United States
Orlando, FL
17 December 2021

11969534R00061